THE BEATLES

PAST MASTERS · VOLUME TWO

Wise Publications
London / New York / Paris / Sydney / Copenhagen / Madrid

Exclusive Distributors:
Music Sales Limited
8/9 Frith Street, London W1V 5TZ, England.
Music Sales Pty Limited
120 Rothschild Avenue, Rosebery,
NSW 2018, Australia.

Order No. NO90641
ISBN 0-7119-5546-8
This book © Copyright 1995 by Wise Publications

Music arranged by Frank Booth
Music processed by MSS Studios
Book design by Studio Twenty
Quarked by Ben May
Photograph courtesy of
London Features International

Printed in the United Kingdom by
J.B. Offset Printers (Marks Tey) Limited, Marks Tey, Essex.

DAY TRIPPER

Words & Music by John Lennon & Paul McCartney

Moderate Rock

Got a good rea - son   for
She's a big teas - er,
Tried __ to please __ her,

It took me so _____ long _____ to find out _____

and I found out.   out.

Ah _____

7

PAPERBACK WRITER

Words & Music by John Lennon & Paul McCartney

Bright Rock

Pa - per - back wri - ter, Pa - per - back wri - ter.

1. Dear __ Sir or Mad - am will you read my book? It took me
(3) thou - sand pag - es, give or take a few; I'll be

years to write; — Will you take a look? It's based on a nov-el by a
writ - ing more — in a week or two. I can make it long - er if you

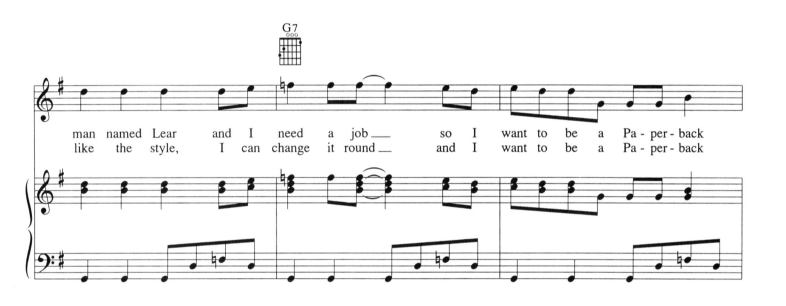

man named Lear and I need a job — so I want to be a Pa - per - back
like the style, I can change it round — and I want to be a Pa - per - back

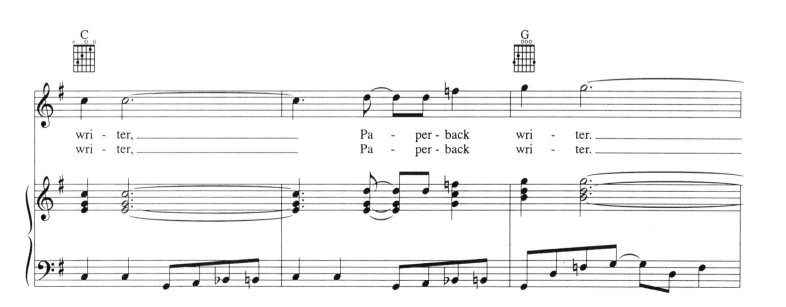

wri - ter, _____ Pa - per - back wri - ter. _____
wri - ter, _____ Pa - per - back wri - ter. _____

2. It's the dir - ty sto - ry of a dir - ty man, ___ and his
4. If you real - ly like it you can have the rights, ___ It could

cling - ing wife ___ does - n't un - der - stand. His son is work - ing for the
make a mil - lion for you ov - er - night. If you must re - turn ___ it, you can

Dai - ly Mail; ___ It's a stead - y job ___ but he wants to be a Pa - per - back
send it here, ___ But I need a break ___ and I want to be a Pa - per - back

wri - ter, _____ Pa - per - back wri - ter. ___
wri - ter, _____ Pa - per - back wri - ter. ___

WE CAN WORK IT OUT

Words & Music by John Lennon & Paul McCartney

RAIN

Words & Music by John Lennon & Paul McCartney

Moderately

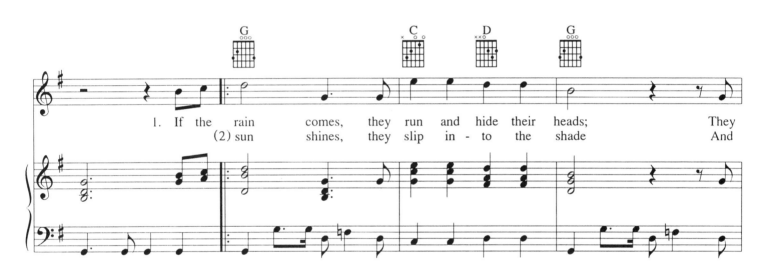

1. If the rain   comes,   they   run   and   hide   their   heads;   They
(2) sun   shines,   they   slip   in - to   the   shade   And

might   as   well   be   dead.   If   the   rain   comes, _____   If   the
sip   their   lem - on - ade.   When   the   sun   shines, _____   when   the

LADY MADONNA

Words & Music by John Lennon & Paul McCartney

Brightly, with a beat

1.4. La - dy Ma - don - na, chil - dren at your feet; ___
2. La - dy Ma - don - na, ba - by at your breast; ___
3. La - dy Ma - don - na, ly - ing on the bed; ___

To Coda ⊕

won - der how you man - age to make ___ ends meet. ___
won - der how you man - age to feed ___ the rest. ___
Lis - ten to the mu - sic play - ing in your head. ___

who finds the mon - ey, when you pay the rent, ___
(Instrumental)
(Instrumental)

Did you think that mon - ey was ___ heav - en sent? ___

Fri - day night ___ ar - rives ___ with - out ___ a suit - case; ___
3. Tues - day af - ter - noon ___ is nev - er end - ing; ___

Sun - day morn - ing creeps in like a nun. ___
Wednes - day morn - ing pa - pers did - n't come. ___

19

Mon - day's child has learned to tie ____ his boot - lace. ____
Thurs - day night your stock - ings need - ed mend - ing. ____

See how they run! ____

D.S. al Coda

Coda

20

THE INNER LIGHT

Words & Music by George Harrison

Moderately

With-

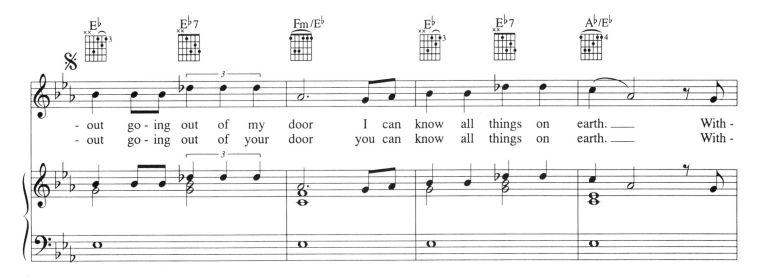

- out go-ing out of my door   I can know all things on earth. ___ With-
- out go-ing out of your door   you can know all things on earth. ___ With-

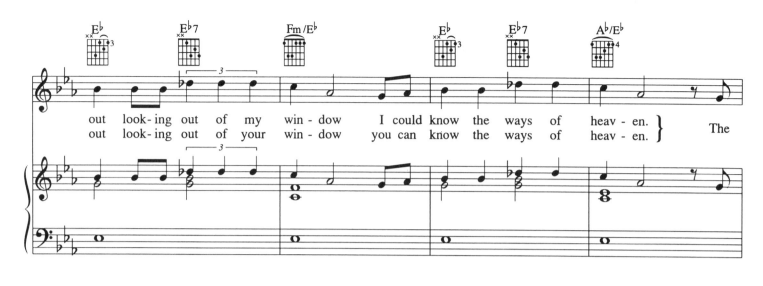

out look-ing out of my win-dow I could know the ways of heav-en.
out look-ing out of your win-dow you can know the ways of heav-en. } The

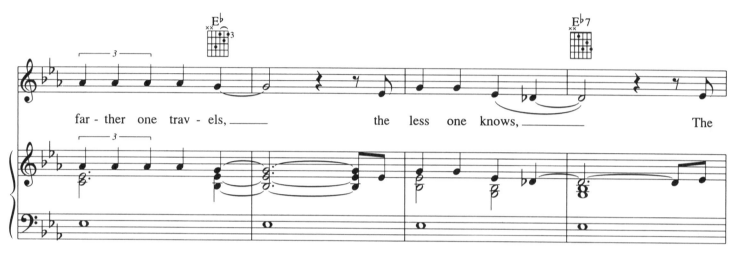

far - ther one trav - els, _____ the less one knows, _____ The

To Coda ⊕

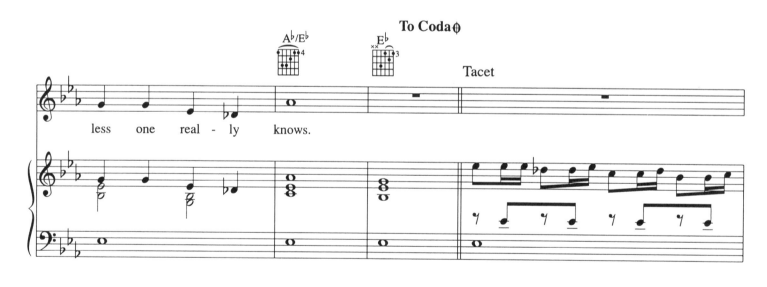

Tacet

less one real - ly knows.

HEY JUDE

Words & Music by John Lennon & Paul McCartney

1. Hey Jude, _____ don't make it bad, Take a
4. Jude, _____ don't make it bad, Take a

sad song _____ and make it bet - ter. _____ Re - mem - ber to let her in - to your
sad song _____ and make it bet - ter. _____ Re - mem - ber to let her un - der your

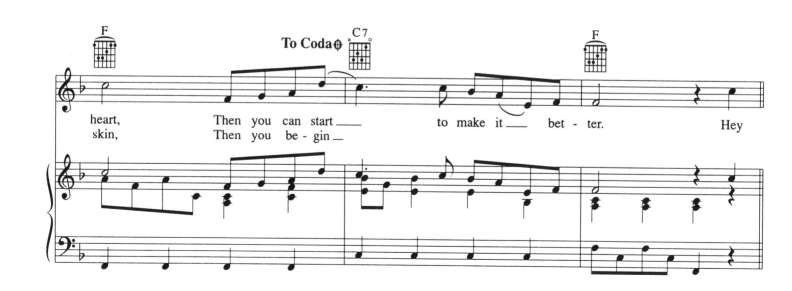

heart, Then you can start _____ to make it _____ bet - ter. Hey
skin, Then you be - gin _____

GET BACK

Words & Music by John Lennon & Paul McCartney

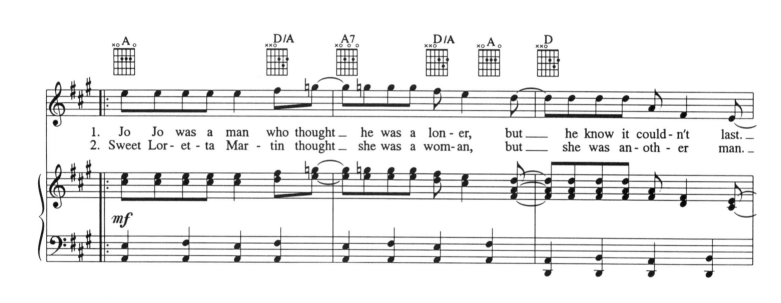

1. Jo Jo was a man who thought he was a lon-er, but he know it could-n't last.
2. Sweet Lor-et-ta Mar-tin thought she was a wom-an, but she was an-oth-er man.

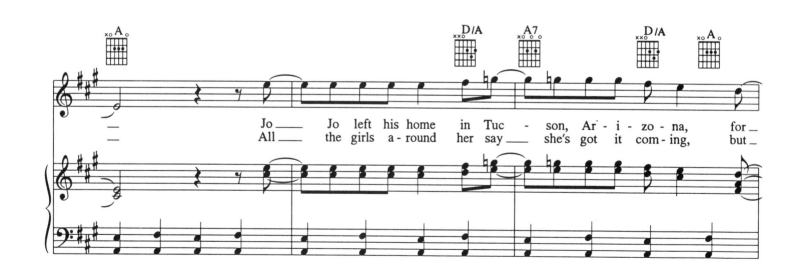

— Jo Jo left his home in Tuc-son, Ar-i-zo-na, for —
— All the girls a-round her say she's got it com-ing, but —

some Cal - i - for - nia grass. ___
she gets it while she can. ___
Get back! ___ Get back! ___

Get back ___ to where you once be - longed. _____ Get back! ___

Get back! ___ Get back ___ to where you once be - longed. ___

(Get back, Jo Jo)

REVOLUTION

Words & Music by John Lennon & Paul McCartney

Moderate Shuffle

1. You

say you want a rev - o - lu - tion, _____ Well _____
(2) say you got a real so - lu - tion, _____ Well _____
(3) say you'll change the con - sti - tu - tion, _____ Well _____

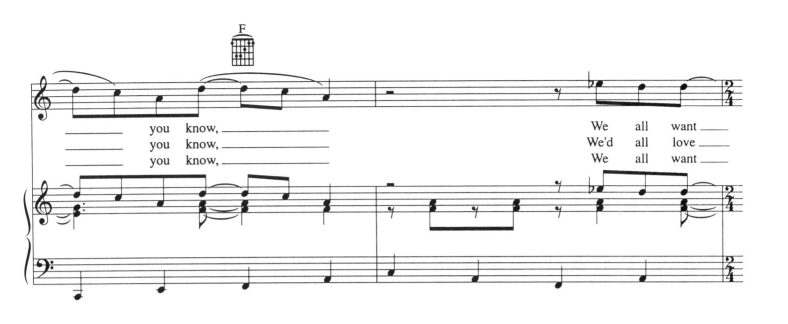

you know, _____ We all want _____
you know, _____ We'd all love _____
you know, _____ We all want _____

_ to change the world.   You
_ to see the plan.   You
_ to change your head.   You

tell me that it's e - vo - lu - tion, _____ Well _____ you know, _____
ask me for a con - tri - bu - tion, _____ Well _____ you know, _____
tell me it's the in - sti - tu - tion, _____ Well _____ you know, _____

We all want _____ to change the world. _____
We're all do - ing what we can. _____
You bet - ter free _____ your mind in - stead. _____

But when you talk a - bout de -
But if you want mon - ey for peo - ple with
But if you go car - ry - ing pic - tures of

struc - tion, _____
minds that hate, _____
Chair - man Mao, _____

Don't you know that you can
All I can tell you is "Broth - er you
You ain't go - ing to make it with an - y - one

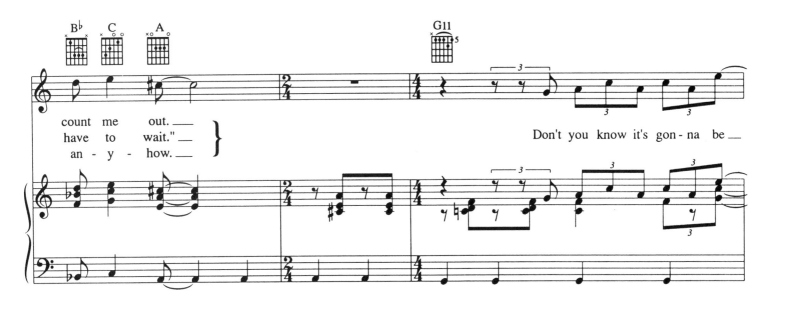

count me out. ___
have to wait." ___
an - y - how. ___

Don't you know it's gon - na be ___

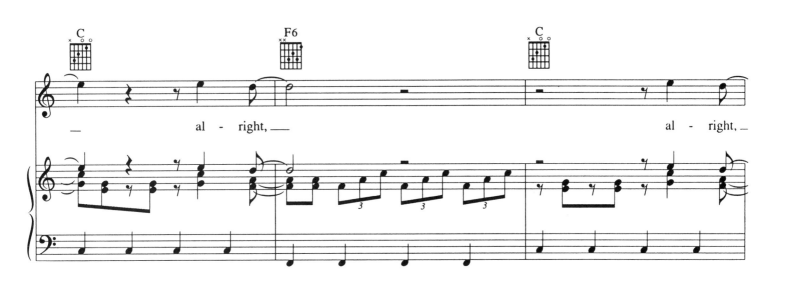

al - right, ___

al - right, ___

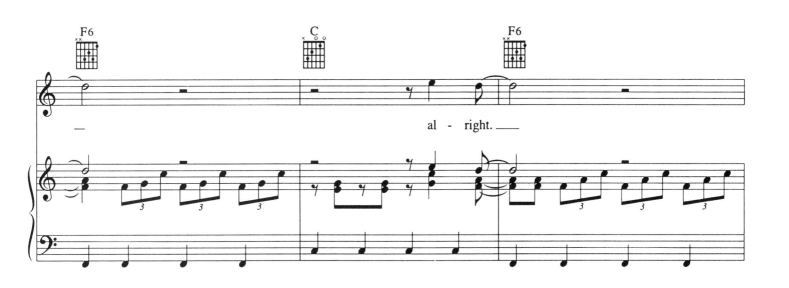

al - right. ___

33

DON'T LET ME DOWN

Words & Music by John Lennon & Paul McCartney

Don't let me down,

Don't let me down. _____

Don't let me down, _____

Don't let me down. _____

Nobod-y ev-er loved me like she
And from the first time that she real-ly

THE BALLAD OF JOHN AND YOKO

Words & Music by John Lennon & Paul McCartney

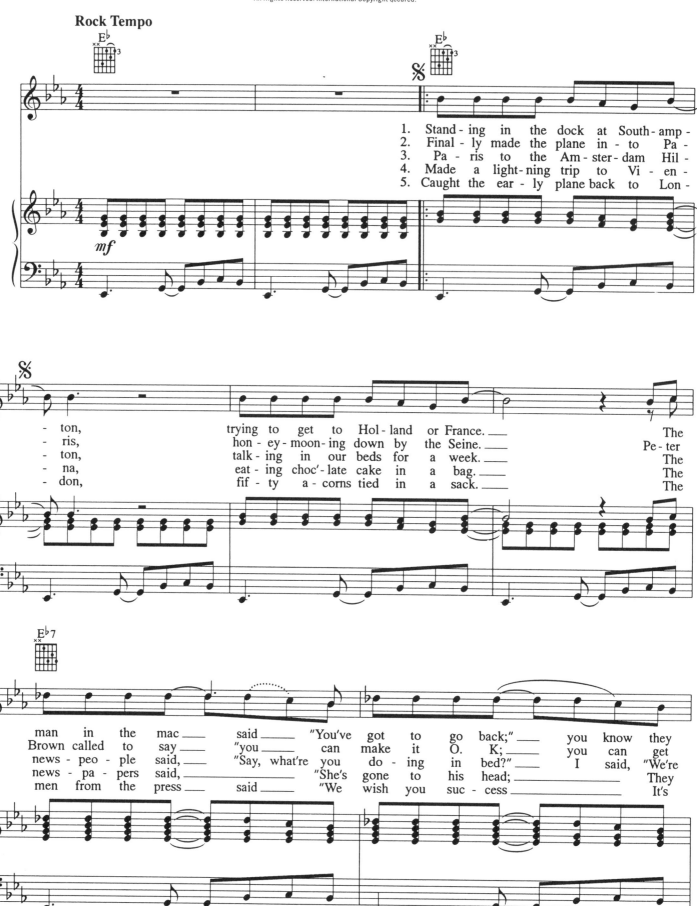

did -n't ev - en give us a chance. __
mar - ried in Gib - ral - tar near Spain. __
on - ly trying to get us some peace." __ } Christ! you know it ain't eas - y, __
look just like two Gu - rus in drag." __
good to have the both of you back." __

you know how hard it can be; __   The way things are go -

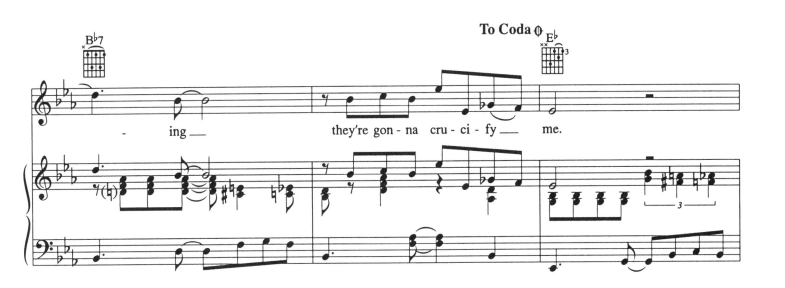

- ing __   they're gon - na cru - ci - fy __ me.

39

3. Drove from

Sav-ing up your mon-ey for a rain - y day, ___ giv-ing all __ your clothes to char-i-

- ty. Last night the wife said, "Oh boy, when you're dead you

OLD BROWN SHOE

Words & Music by George Harrison

Bright Shuffle

1. I want a love that's right, ___ right ___ is on - ly half of what's wrong. ___
(2) pick me up ___ from where ___ some try to drag me down. ___
(3) Love is yours; ___ to miss ___ that love is some - thing I'd hate. ___

— I want a short - haired girl ___ who
— And when I see you smile ___ re -
— I'll make an ear - ly start, ___ I'm

some - times wears it twice as long. _____ Now
-plac - ing ev - 'ry thought - less frown. _____ For
mak - ing sure that I'm not late. _____

F   **A♭**

I'm step - pin' out this old _____ brown shoe, _____ Ba - by I'm in
Got me es - cap - ing from _____ this zoo, _____ Ba - by I'm in
your sweet top lip I'm in _____ the queue, _____ Ba - by I'm in

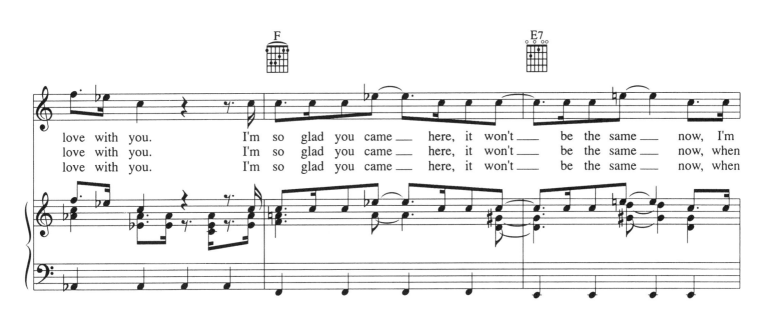

F   **E7**

love with you. I'm so glad you came _____ here, it won't _____ be the same _____ now, I'm
love with you. I'm so glad you came _____ here, it won't _____ be the same _____ now, when
love with you. I'm so glad you came _____ here, it won't _____ be the same _____ now, when

ACROSS THE UNIVERSE

Words & Music by John Lennon & Paul McCartney

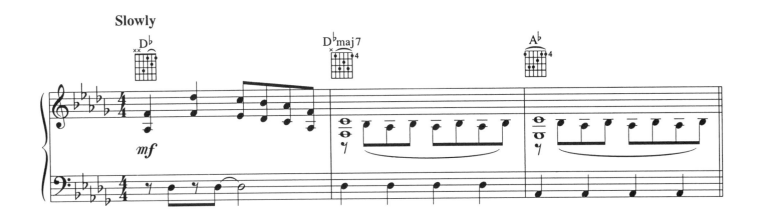

Words are fly-ing out __ like end-less rain __ in-to a pa-per cup, __ They

slith-er while, _ they pass, they slip a-way _____ a-cross the u-ni-verse. _

tum - ble blind - ly as they make their way a - cross the u - ni - verse

D.S. al Coda

Coda

Sounds of laugh - ter, shades of earth are ring - ing through my o - pened ears, In -

- cit - ing and in - vit - ing me. Lim - it - less, un - dy - ing love, which

shines a - round me like a mil - lion suns, And calls me on and on a - cross the u - ni - verse.

51

LET IT BE

Words & Music by John Lennon & Paul McCartney

Slowly

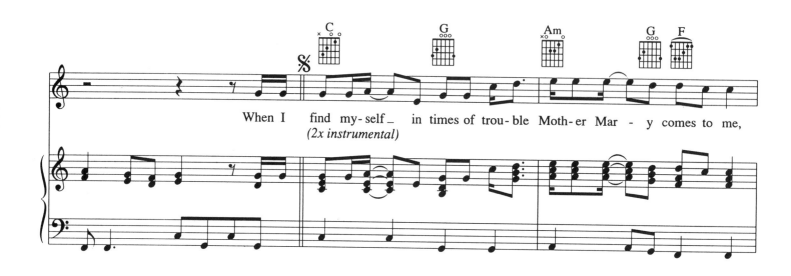

When I find my-self _ in times of trou-ble Moth-er Mar - y comes to me,
(2x instrumental)

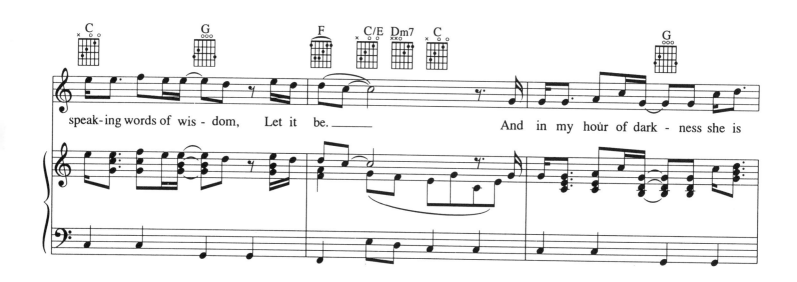

speak-ing words of wis - dom, Let it be. _____ And in my hour of dark - ness she is

YOU KNOW MY NAME (LOOK UP THE NUMBER)

Words & Music by John Lennon & Paul McCartney